I'll Wait, Mr. Panda

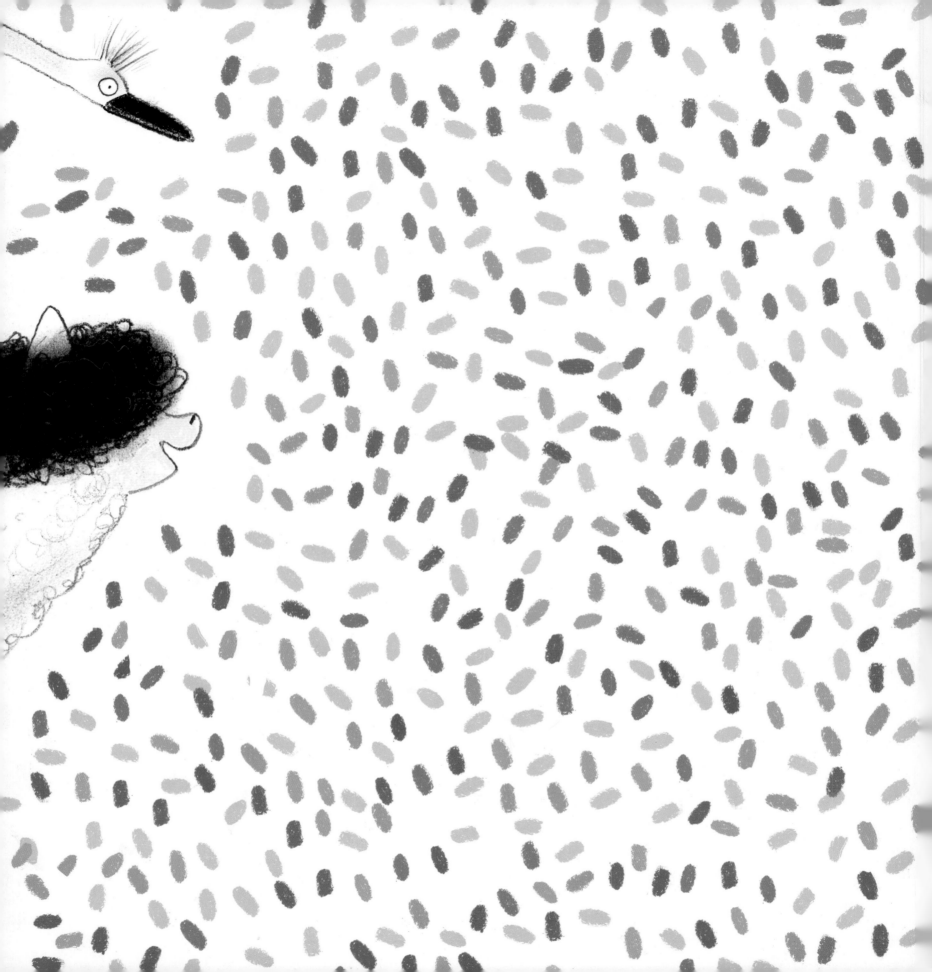

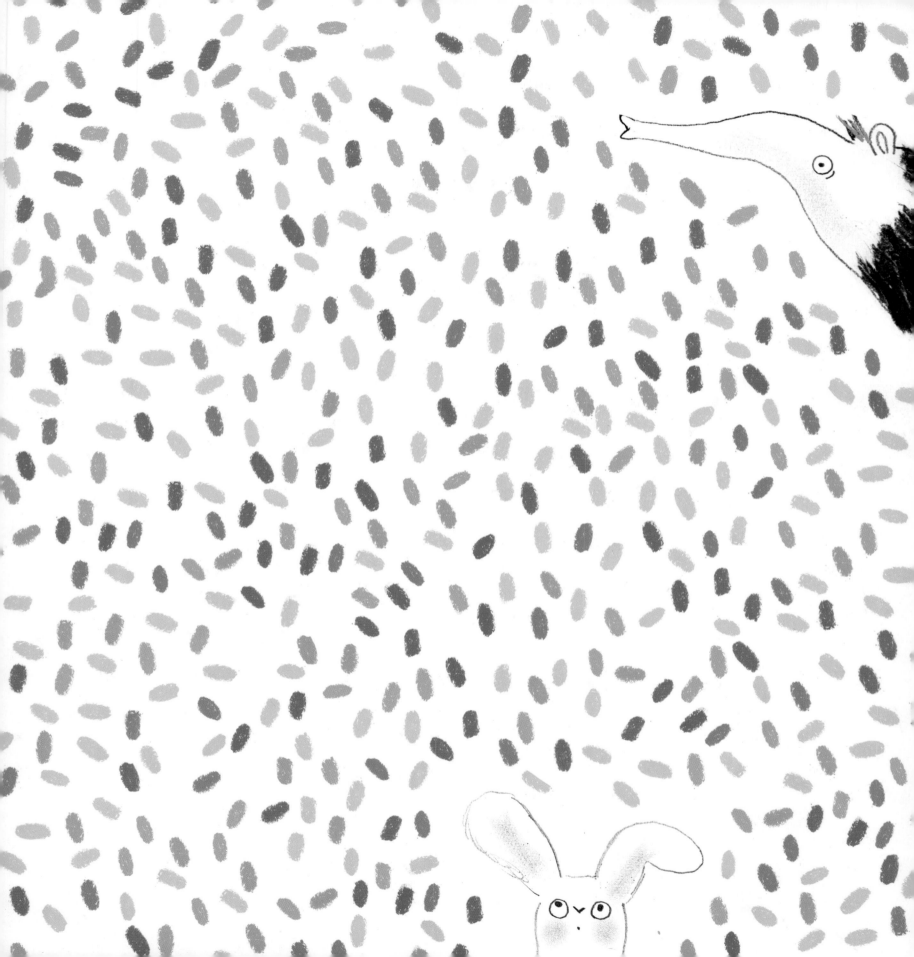

To Dad

I'll Wait, Mr. Panda

Steve Antony

SCHOLASTIC INC.

What are
you making,
Mr. Panda?

No, I will not wait.
Good-bye.

Are you
making cookies,
Mr. Panda?

Wait and see. It's a surprise.

No, waiting
is too hard.
Good-bye.

I'll wait, Mr. Panda.

No,
I'm done
waiting.

Is it ready yet, Mr. Panda?

No, wait here.

I don't like waiting

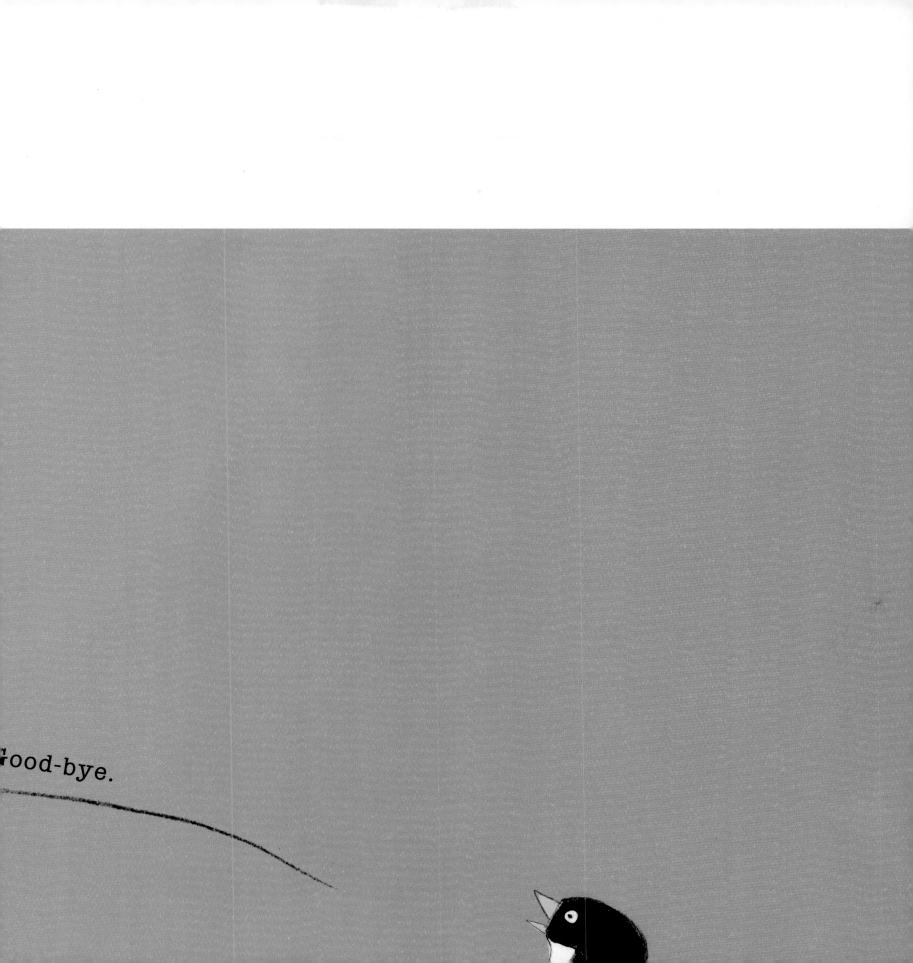

ood-bye.

I'll wait,
Mr. Panda!

I'm waiting, Mr. Panda.

WOW!
That was worth the wait.

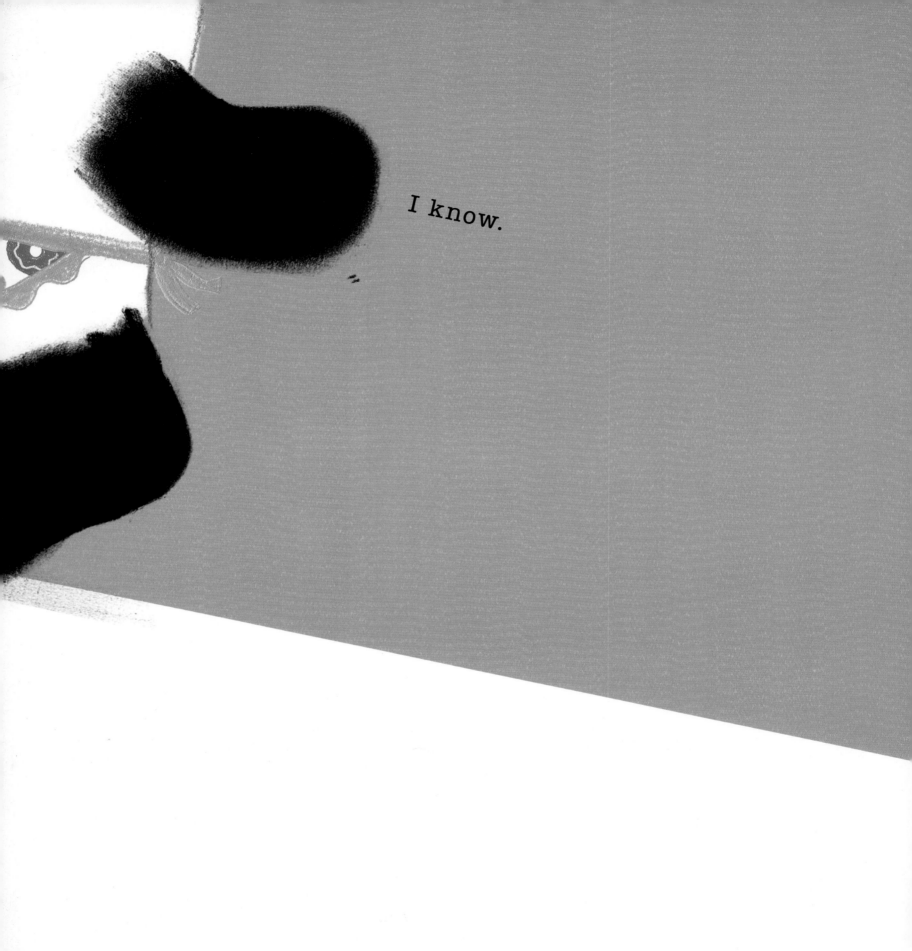

I know.

Thank you, Mr. Panda.
I can't wait to eat it!